The Red Book
Alto Saxophone

© 2010 by Faber Music Ltd
First published in 2010 by Faber Music Ltd
Bloomsbury House 74–77 Great Russell Street London WC1B 3DA
Music processed by MusicSet 2000
Printed in England by Caligraving Ltd
All rights reserved

ISBN10: 0-571-53508-9
EAN13: 978-0-571-53508-8

To buy Faber Music publications or to find out about the full range of titles available,
please contact your local music retailer or Faber Music sales enquiries:

Faber Music Ltd, Burnt Mill, Elizabeth Way, Harlow, CM20 2HX England
Tel: +44(0)1279 82 89 82 Fax: +44(0)1279 82 89 83
sales@fabermusic.com fabermusic.com

The Red Book

Alto Saxophone

DON'T RAIN ON MY PARADE

Words by Bob Merrill   Music by Jule Styne

EMPIRE STATE OF MIND (PART II) BROKEN DOWN

Words and Music by Sylvia Robinson, Bert Keyes, Shawn Carter, Angela Hunte,
Alicia Augello-Cook, Janet Sewell and Al Shuckburgh

EVERYBODY HURTS

Words and Music by William Berry, Michael Stipe, Peter Buck and Michael Mills

HOME

Words and Music by Michael Bublé, Amy Foster-Gillies and Alan Chang

2nd time to Coda

I'LL STAND BY YOU

Words and Music by Chrissie Hynde, Tom Kelly and Billy Steinberg

I SAY A LITTLE PRAYER

Words by Hal David   Music by Burt Bacharach

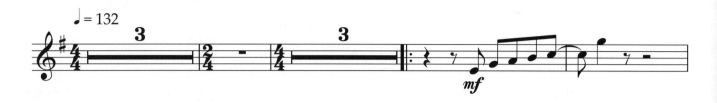

ISN'T SHE LOVELY

Words and Music by Stevie Wonder

NELLA FANTASIA

Words by Chiara Ferrau   Music by Ennio Morricone

LET'S FACE THE MUSIC AND DANCE

Words and Music by Irving Berlin

TRACK

THE LOCO-MOTION

Words and Music by Gerry Goffin and Carole King

MATERIAL GIRL

Words and Music by Peter Brown and Robert Rans

MERCY

Words and Music by Duffy and Stephen Booker

SHE'S SO LOVELY

Words and Music by Roy Stride

SMELLS LIKE TEEN SPIRIT

Words and Music by Kurt Cobain, David Grohl and Chris Novoselic

YOU'RE BEAUTIFUL

Words and Music by James Blunt, Sacha Skarbek and Amanda Ghost

Selections from

SHAKESPEARE IN LOVE

Original music composed & orchestrated by Stephen Warbeck,
arranged for solo piano by Derek Jones.

Sony/ATV Music Publishing (UK) Limited

The Beginning of the Partnership

COMPOSED BY STEPHEN WARBECK

It was a lover and his lass,
With a hey and a ho and a hey nonino,
That o'er the green corn-field did pass,
In spring-time, the only pretty ring-time,
When birds do sing, hey ding a ding, ding,
Sweet lovers love the spring.

Between the acres of the rye,
With a hey and a ho and a hey nonino,
These pretty country-folks would lie,
In spring-time, the only pretty ring-time,
When birds do sing, hey ding a ding, ding,
Sweet lovers love the spring.

This carol they began that hour,
With a hey and a ho and a hey nonino,
How that a life was but a flower,
In spring-time, the only pretty ring-time,
When birds do sing, hey ding a ding, ding,
Sweet lovers love the spring.

And therefore take the present time,
With a hey and a ho and a hey nonino,
For love is crowned with the prime,
In spring-time, the only pretty ring-time,
When birds do sing, hey ding a ding, ding,
Sweet lovers love the spring.

As You Like It
Act V Scene III

Viola's Audition

COMPOSED BY STEPHEN WARBECK

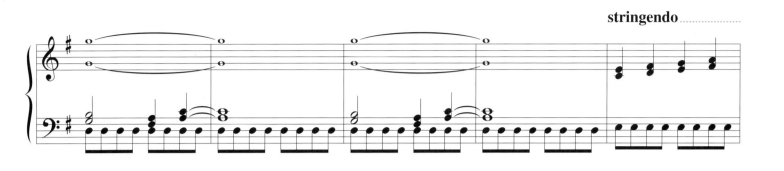

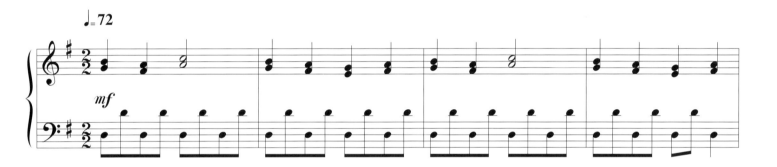

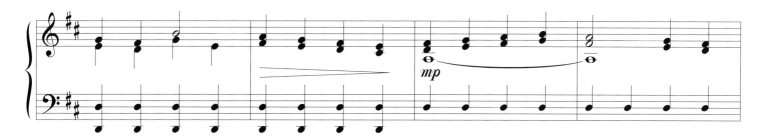

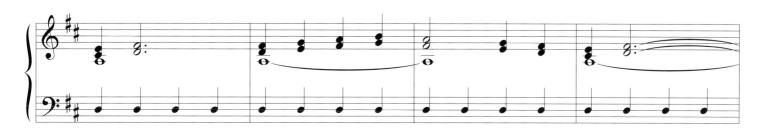

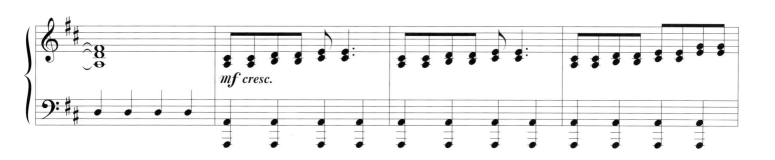

Oh mistress mine! where are you roaming?
O, stay and hear; your true love's coming,
That can sing both high and low.
Trip no further, pretty sweeting;
Journeys end in lovers meeting,
Every wise man's son doth know.

What is love? 'tis not hereafter;
Present mirth hath present laughter;
What's to come is still unsure:
In delay there lies no plenty;
Then come kiss me, sweet and twenty,
Youth's a stuff will not endure.

Twelfth Night
Act II Scene III

The De Lessep's Dance

COMPOSED BY STEPHEN WARBECK

Repeat 3 times ad lib.

A New World

COMPOSED BY STEPHEN WARBECK

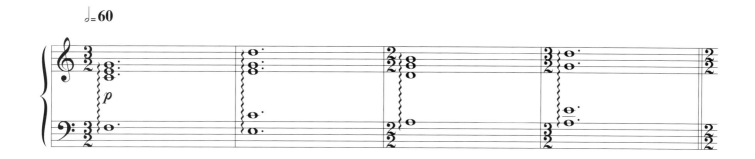

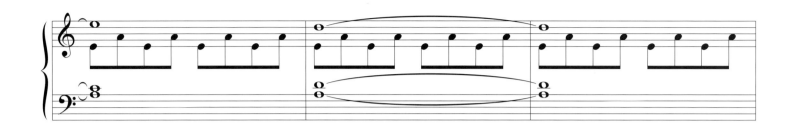

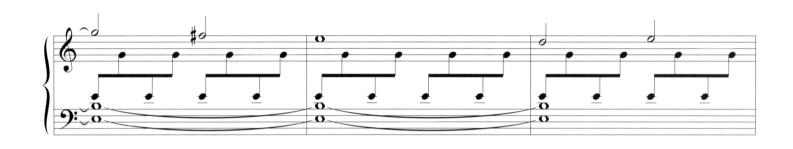

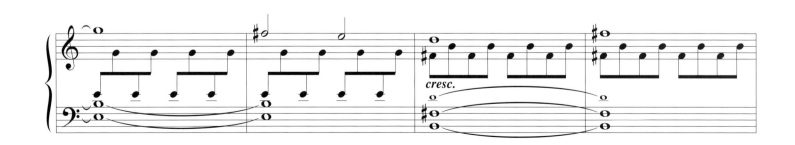

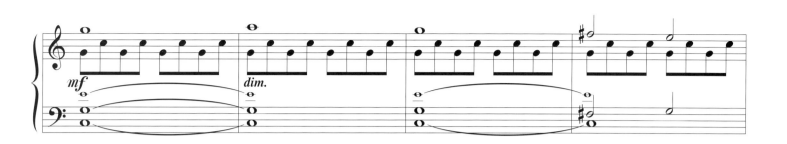

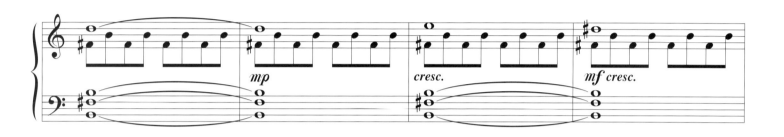

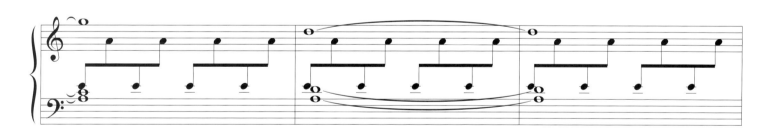

Take, O take those lips away,
That so sweetly were forsworn;
And those eyes, the break of day,
Lights that do mislead the morn;
But my kisses bring again, bring again;
Seal of love, but sealed in vain,
Sealed in vain.

Measure For Measure
Act IV Scene I

Who is Sylvia? What is she,
That all our swains commend her?
Holy, fair, and wise is she;
The heaven such grace did lend her,
That she might admired be.

Is she kind as she is fair?
For beauty lives with kindness.
Love doth to her eyes repair,
To help him of his blindness,
And, being helped, inhabits there.

Then to Sylvia let us sing,
That Sylvia is excelling.
She excels each mortal thing
Upon the dull earth dwelling;
To her let us garlands bring.

The Two Gentlemen of Verona
Act IV Scene II

The Arrival of Wessex

COMPOSED BY STEPHEN WARBECK

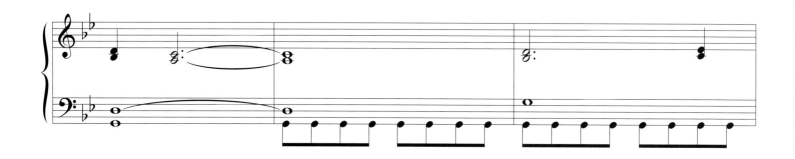

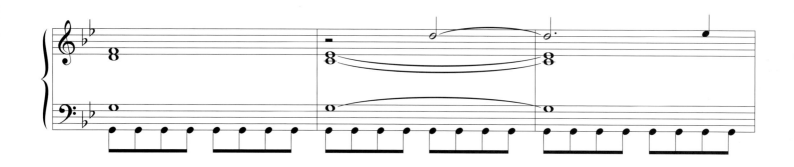

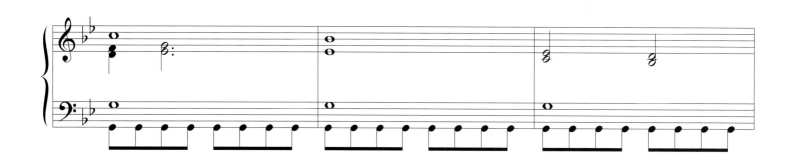

Greenwich

COMPOSED BY STEPHEN WARBECK

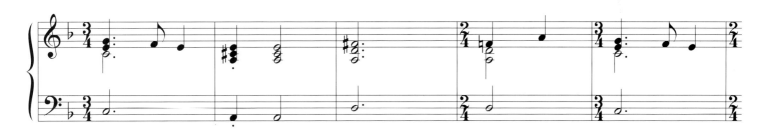

rit.

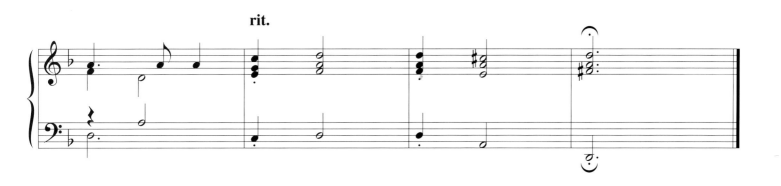

18

Shall I compare thee to a summer's day?
Thou art more lovely and more temperate:
Rough winds do shake the darling buds of May,
And summer's lease hath all too short a date.
Sometime too hot the eye of heaven shines,
And often is his gold complexion dimmed;
And every fair from fair sometime declines,
By chance, or nature's changing course untrimmed;
By thy eternal summer shall not fade,
Nor lose possession of that fair thou ow'st,
Nor shall death brag thou wander'st in his shade,
When in eternal lines to time thou grow'st,
So long as men can breathe, or eyes can see,
So long lives this, and this gives life to thee.

98

From you have I been absent in the spring,
When proud-pied April, dressed in all his trim,
Hath put a spirit of youth in everything,
That heavy Saturn laughed and leaped with him,
Yet nor the lays of birds, nor the sweet smell
Of different flowers in odor and in hue,
Could make me any summer's story tell,
Or from their proud lap pluck them where they grew.
Nor praise the deep vermilion in the rose;
They were but sweet, but figures of delight,
Drawn after you, you pattern of all those.
Yet seemed it winter still, and, you away,
As with your shadow I with these did play.

The Play & the Marriage

COMPOSED BY STEPHEN WARBECK

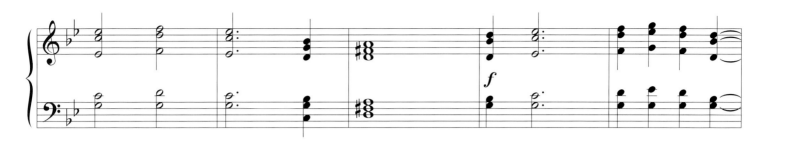

116

Let me not to the marriage of true minds
Admit impediments; love is not love
Which alters when it alteration finds
Or bends with the remover to remove.
O, no, it is an ever-fixed mark
That looks on tempests and is never shaken;
It is the star to every wand'ring bark,
Whose worth's unknown, although his height be taken.
Love's not Time's fool, though rosy lips and cheeks
Within his bending sickle's compass come;
Love alters not with his brief hours and weeks,
But bears it out even to the edge of doom.
If this be error, and upon me proved,
I never writ, nor no man ever loved.

Curtain Call

COMPOSED BY STEPHEN WARBECK

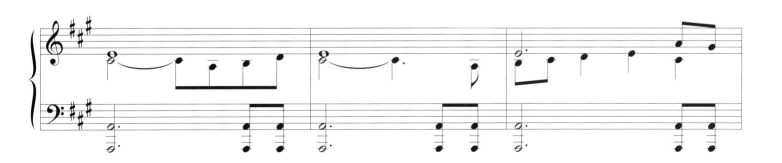

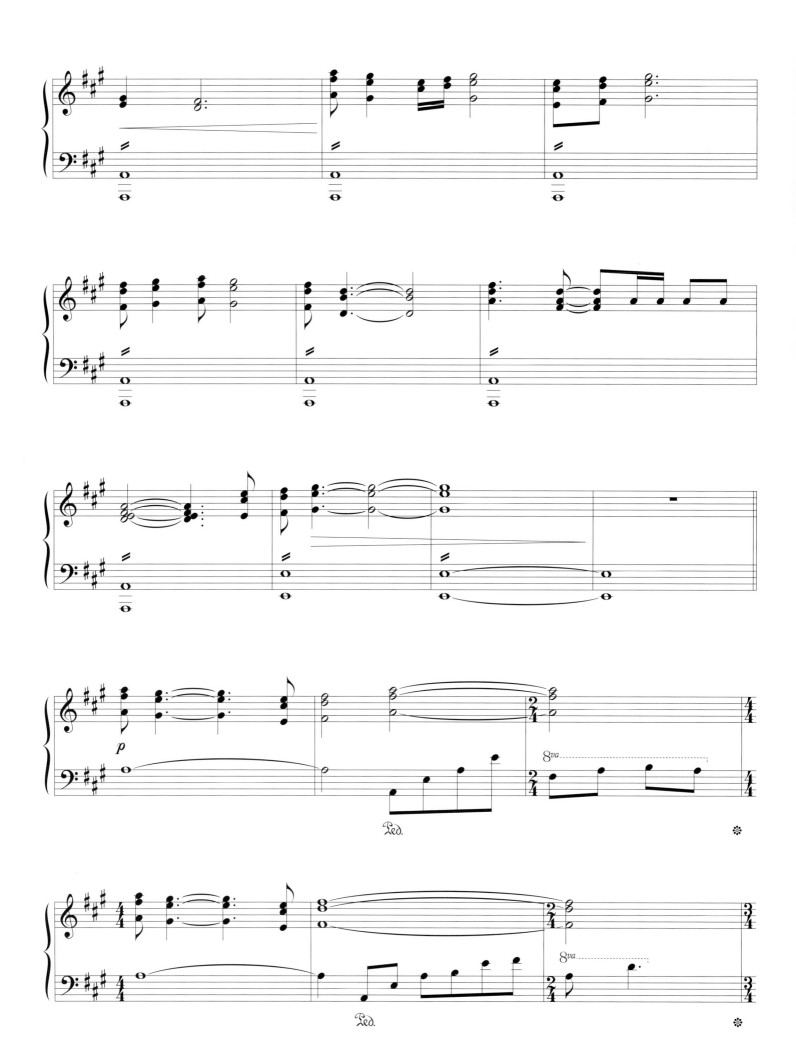

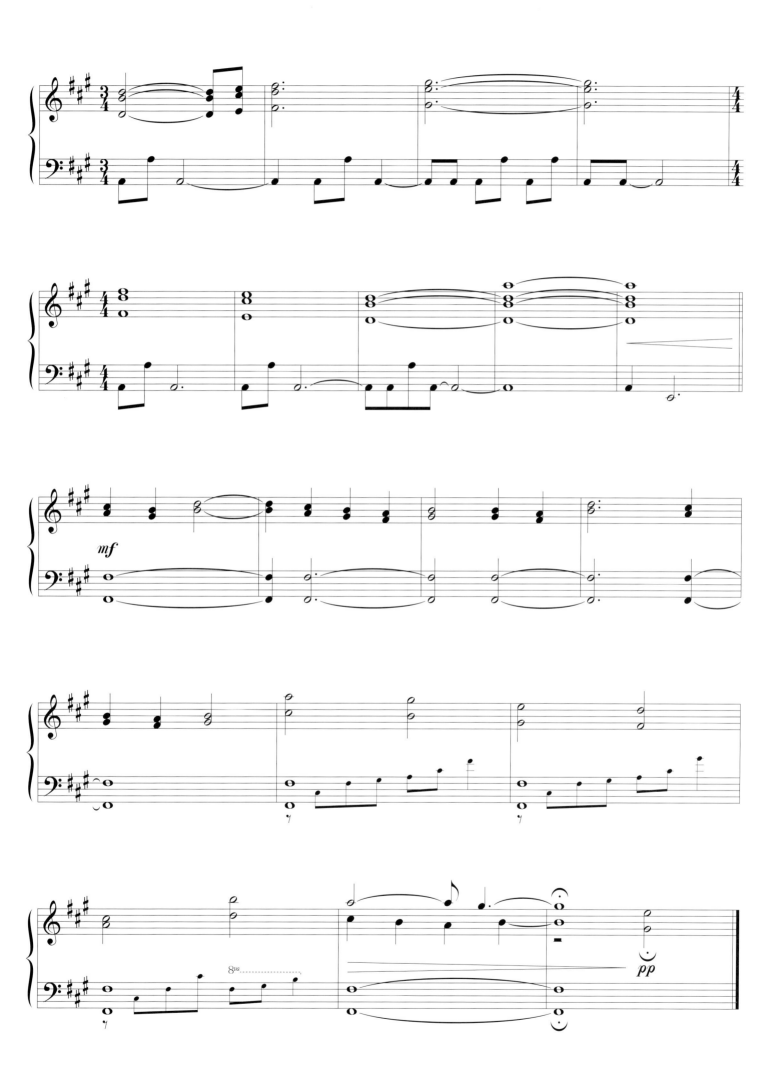

130

My mistress' eyes are nothing like the sun;
Coral is far more red than her lips' red.
If snow be white, why then her breasts are dun;
If hairs be wires, black wires grow on her head.
I have seen roses damasked, red and white,
But no such roses see I in her cheeks;
And in some perfumes is there more delight
Than in the breath that from my mistress reeks.
I love to hear her speak; yet well I know
That music hath a far more pleasing sound.
I grant I never saw a goddess go;
My mistress, when she walks, treads on the ground.
And yet, by heaven, I think my love as rare
As any she belied with false compare.

The End

COMPOSED BY STEPHEN WARBECK

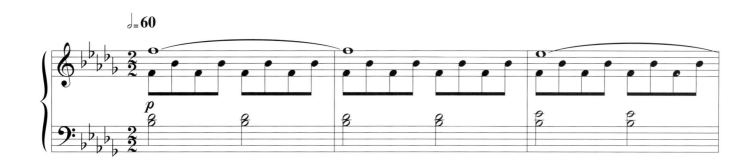

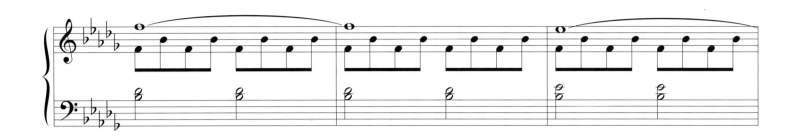

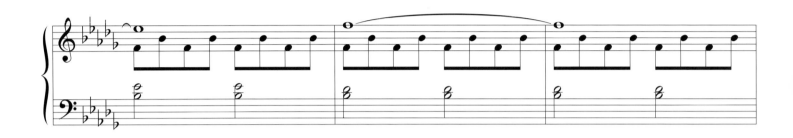

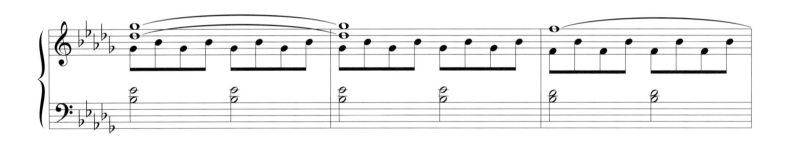

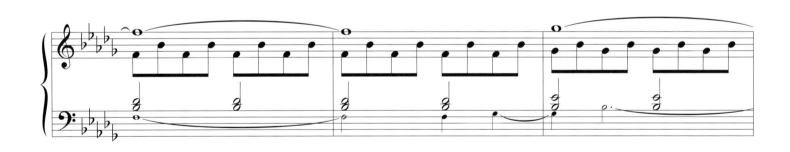

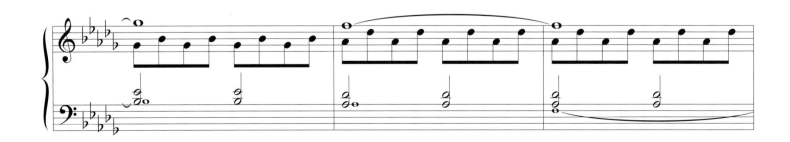

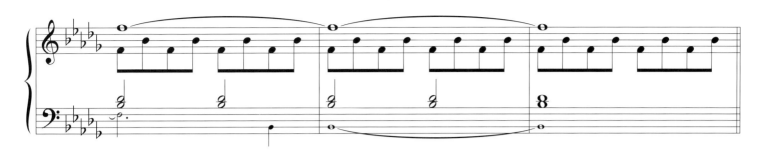
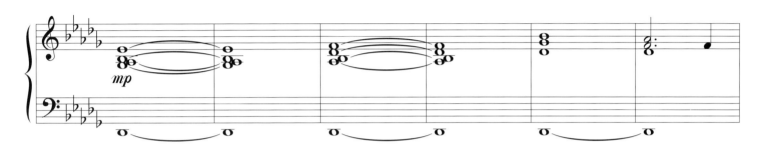

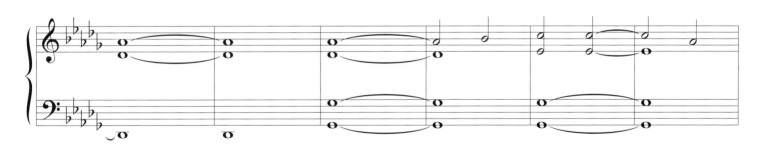
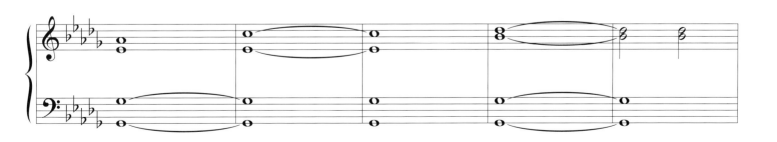

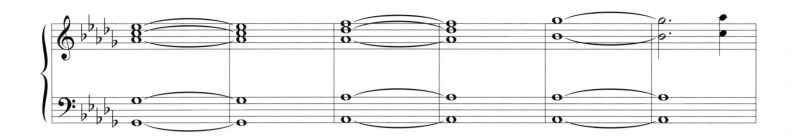

cresc. poco a poco

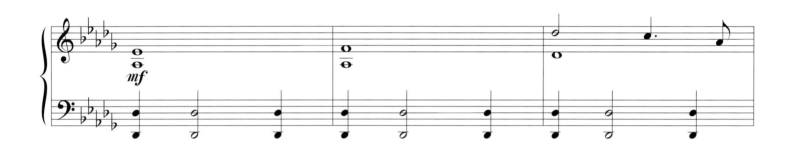

mf

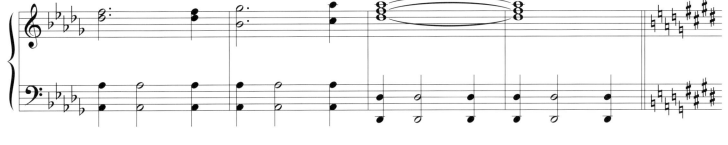

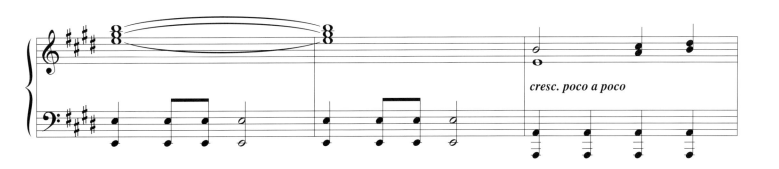

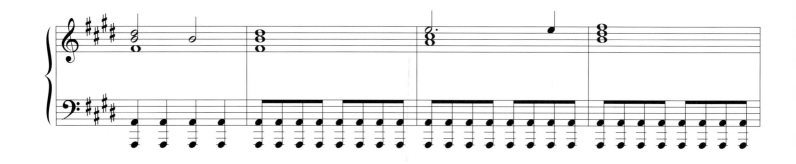

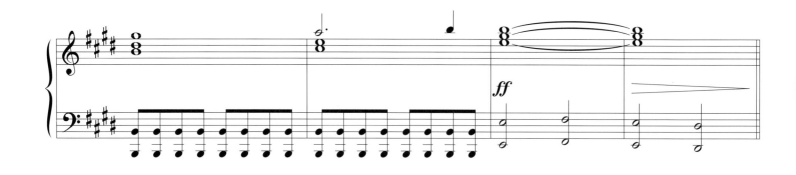

Exclusive Distributors:
Music Sales Limited
8/9 Frith Street, London W1V 5TZ,
England.

Music Sales Pty Limited
120 Rothschild Avenue, Rosebery, NSW 2018,
Australia.

Order No. AM959167
ISBN 0-7119-7416-0
This book © Copyright 1999 by Sony/
ATV Music Publishing (UK) Limited.
www.internetmusicshop.co.uk

Music arranged by Derek Jones.
Music processed by Paul Ewers Music Design.
Book design by Michael Bell Design.
Photographs © Copyright 1998 courtesy of Miramax Films.
Printed in the United Kingdom by
Caligraving Limited, Thetford, Norfolk.

Your Guarantee of Quality:
As publishers, we strive to produce every
book to the highest commercial standards.
The music has been freshly engraved
and the book has been carefully designed to
minimise awkward page turns and to make
playing from it a real pleasure.
Particular care has been given to specifying
acid-free, neutral-sized paper made from pulps
which have not been elemental chlorine bleached.
This pulp is from farmed sustainable
forests and was produced with special
regard for the environment.
Throughout, the printing and binding
have been planned to ensure a sturdy, attractive
publication which should give years of enjoyment.
If your copy fails to meet our high standards, please
inform us and we will gladly replace it.

Music Sales' complete catalogue describes
thousands of titles and is available in full colour
sections by subject, direct from Music Sales Limited.
Please state your areas of interest and send
a cheque/postal order for £1.50 for postage to:
Music Sales Limited, Newmarket Road,
Bury St. Edmunds, Suffolk IP33 3YB.